This book belongs to:

Baby Shark: Annual 2022
A CENTUM BOOK 978-1-913865-68-9
Published in Great Britain by Centum Books Ltd
This edition published 2021
1 3 5 7 9 10 8 6 4 2

Centum Books Ltd, 20 Devon Square, Newton Abbot, Devon, TQ12 2HR, UK
9/10 Fenian St, Dublin 2, D02 RX24, Ireland.
books@centumbooksltd.co.uk
CENTUM BOOKS Limited Reg. No. 07641486
A CIP catalogue record for this book is available from the British Library.
Printed in China.

pinkfong
BABY SHARK™
2022
ANNUAL

centum

Contents

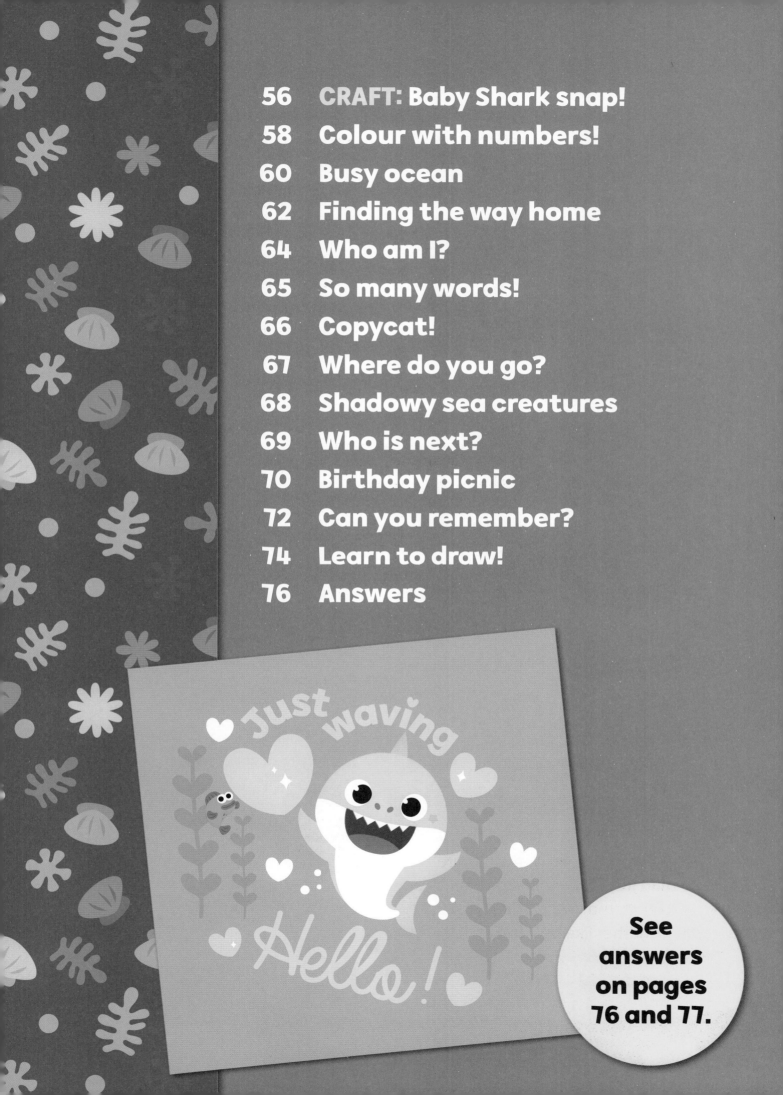

Just waving Hello!

See answers on pages 76 and 77.

Hello Sharks!

Read about your favourite shark family!

Baby Shark

Baby Shark lives under the ocean and is curious about everything around him. He likes to sing. When he's scared, he sings to help him feel brave.

Mummy Shark

There are no limits to the things that Mummy Shark can do! She always listens to Baby Shark and they share a very special bond.

 William

Baby Seahorse

Daddy Shark

Daddy Shark is a strong and mighty hunter. He is much more than just Baby Shark's father though, the two of them play together like best friends!

Grandma Shark

Grandma Shark likes to read. She is a kind and thoughtful grandma who always has time to spend with Baby Shark.

Grandpa Shark

Grandpa Shark is wise and smart. He is famous for his hot clam buns and he loves to share his love of cooking with Baby Shark.

There are so many sea creatures for Baby Shark to play with!

Baby Turtle

Baby Whale

Number colouring!

Can you complete the picture by colouring the numbers the right colours? Make sure you get them all!

⚪	1	Yellow
⚫	2	Orange
⚫	3	Red
⚫	4	Pink
⚫	5	Light pink
⚫	6	Blue
⚫	7	Green
⚫	8	Black
⚪	9	White

You are fintastic

Half and half

Oh no! Half of the picture of Baby Shark is missing. Can you draw the other half? Then you can colour it in!

Best friends!

Baby Shark's best friend is William. He's good friends with Baby Turtle, Baby Seahorse and Baby Whale too. Who are your good friends?

William
Best friend!

Baby Shark
Me!

Best Shark Friend Ever

Baby Seahorse

We like to blow bubbles together!

Baby Whale

We like to play on the seesaw together!

Baby Turtle

We like to play with balloons together!

Follow the arrows and trace over William's name.

William

12

Write your best friends' names (or get a grown-up to help you) and draw a picture of each of them in the boxes. What do you like to do together?

Name:..

We like to ....
....

Name:..

We like to ....
....

Name:..

We like to ....
....

Name:..

We like to ....
....

Guess who?

Baby Shark likes to do jigsaw puzzles and work out what the picture will be. Who do you think this is? What piece goes where?

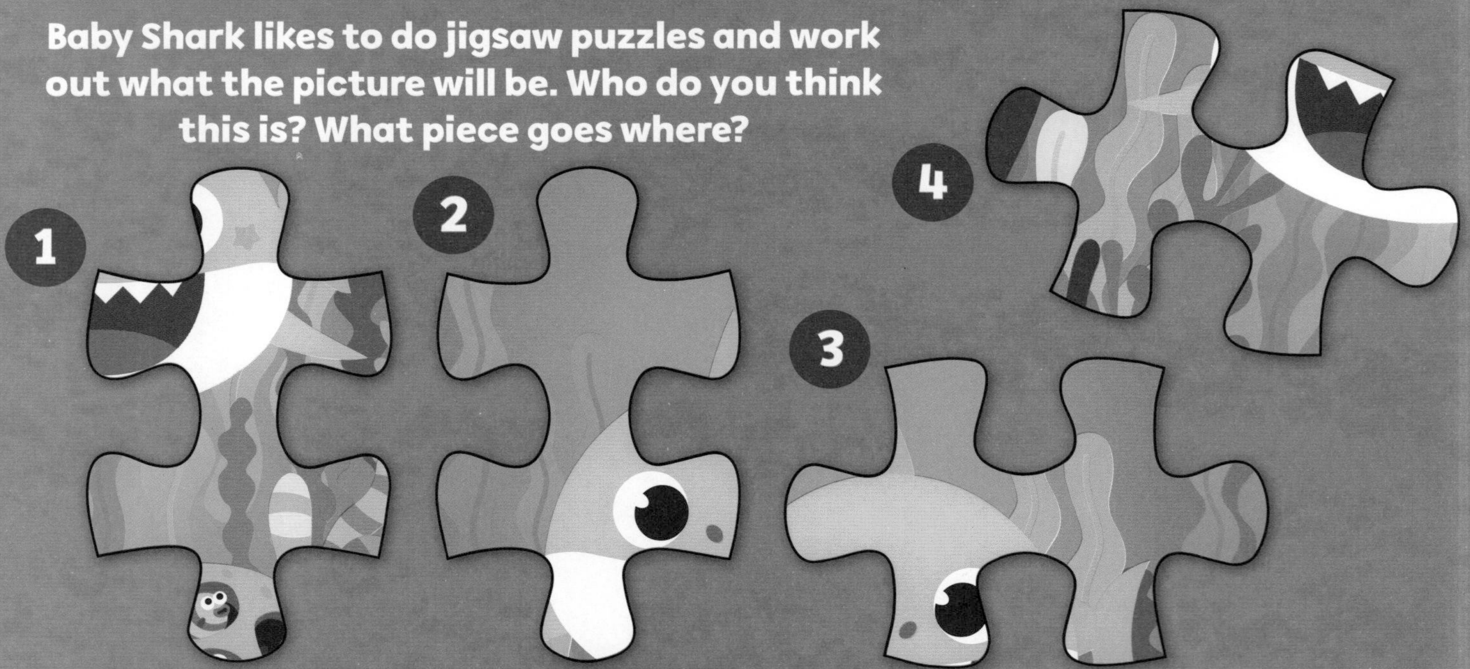

1

2

4

3

a.

b.

c.

d.

Who did it?

Baby Shark's cake has been hidden as a surprise. Who hid it? Work it out by answering the questions below.

The person who hid the cake does not have a ball.

The person who hid the cake does not have sunglasses.

The person who hid the cake is not wearing a hat.

The person who hid the cake is not sitting down.

_____ hid the cake.

15

Baby Shark and the Tooth Fairy

'Good morning!' says Baby Shark, beaming
with a smile as bright as the sun.
Wait a minute, is Baby Shark missing a tooth?

'Oh no!
My tooth!'

Did Baby Shark put it somewhere to hide
it from tooth thieves?
Did Baby Shark put it somewhere safe until
he chomps down on his next hot clam bun?
'Oh no! I'm missing a tooth!' says Baby Shark.
Yes, Baby Shark, you are!

Is his missing tooth under this big rock?

Or is it hidden in this sandcastle?

Baby Shark looks here, there and everywhere!

'Where could it be?' wonders Baby Shark.

'Is it here?

Or here?'

'Does anyone have
an extra tooth this morning?'

21

At first, Baby Shark is mad that he's lost his tooth, and then he feels afraid.

'What am I going to tell Mummy Shark?
And what if I lose another?'

Continued on page 32...

Treasure hunt

Baby Shark is trying to find some treasure. Draw a line between each clue to help him.

Clues

1
2
3
4
5
6
7
8
9
10

START

FINISH

25

Where are all the words?

Can you find the ocean words in the wordsearch below?

SEA
SAND
FISH
SHIP
WHALE
FIN

S	E	A	V	W
A	F	I	S	H
N	I	P	H	A
D	N	W	I	L
K	S	J	P	E

Crack the code

Can you work out the message that Daddy Shark has left for Baby Shark?

Follow the letters and write every third letter down in the space provided.

START

BABY SHARK

THIS WAY

_ _ _ _ _ _ _

_ _ _ _ _ _

27

Family portraits

Baby Shark has drawn all his family and put the pictures in frames. Can you draw your family in the frames provided too? Make sure you colour them all in!

Daddy Shark

Mummy Shark

Grandma Shark

Grandpa Shark

Count me in!

The ocean is full of sea creatures swimming around.

Can you find...

6	4	1	2	8

30

5

3

7

10

9

That night, Baby Shark had a dream that all his teeth ran away.

'Don't leave me toothless,' he cried.

But try as he might, Baby Shark could not catch his teeth.

Without any teeth, he looked just like his grandma!

The next morning when Baby Shark woke up, he still felt sad. He had no choice but to tell his mum the news.

'Mum . . . Mum . . . I'm missing a tooth!'

'Oh, dear me! Don't worry, little one!' says Mummy Shark. 'The Tooth Fairy must have your missing tooth!' 'The Tooth Fairy?' asks Baby Shark.

'Yes, the Tooth Fairy takes the teeth you lose and brings you new ones,' says Mummy Shark.

Mummy Shark hugs Baby Shark tightly and starts to sing a song for him.

'Baby Shark, doo-doo-doo-doo-doo-doo.

Sharp and bright
tooth-tooth-tooth-tooth- tooth.'

Continued on page 48...

Make your own Baby Shark ocean!

You will need the following things to do this fun craft activity.

MATERIALS

- A cereal box
- Scissors
- Some card or paper to draw sea creatures on
- Pens or paints to decorate
- Some string to tie the sea creatures so they look like they are floating
- Glue or sellotape

INSTRUCTIONS

Step 1:

Cut a square section out of the top of the cereal box. Paint the outsides of the box.

Make sure an adult helps you when using scissors and paint!

Step 2:

Decorate inside the back and sides of the box so it looks like an ocean scene. You can just colour it blue or add rocks and seaweed if you like.

Step 3:

Use the Baby Shark characters on the next page and cut them out. Or you can draw your own. Make a little circle at the top of them so you know where the string will go when they are hung up.

Step 4:

Put string through the top of the sea creatures and stick to the inside top of the box with glue or sellotape. Space the creatures out well so they have lots of space to swim.

Use the seafloor as the background for your ocean scene.

Make sure an adult helps you when using scissors!

Use the seafloor as the background for your ocean scene.

Make sure an adult helps you when using scissors!

Count the sea creatures

Baby Shark loves to spot the different colours of the sea creatures and count how many he can see.

How many...?

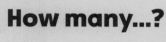

All good friends!

Baby Shark loves to play hide and seek with his friends. Can you find them all? There are some clues below.

Baby Seahorse is near a blue rock with holes.

William is near a yellow plant.

Baby Turtle is near a red piece of seaweed.

Baby Whale is near a green rock.

That's not right!

Something is wrong in each line! What shouldn't be here?
Draw a circle round each one with a pen.

1

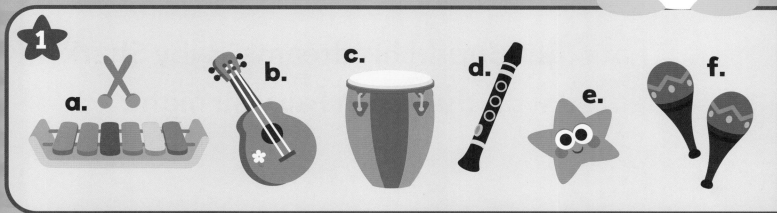

a.   b.   c.   d.   e.   f.

2

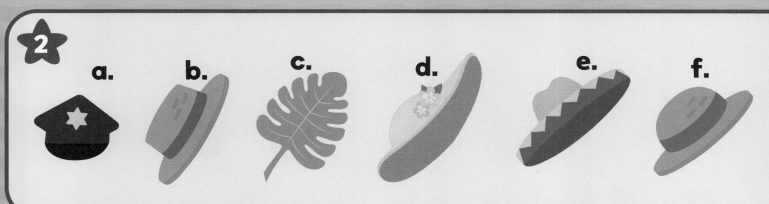

a.   b.   c.   d.   e.   f.

3

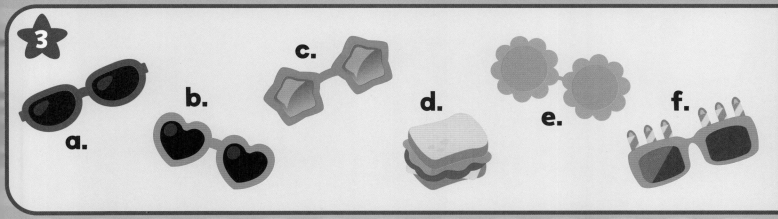

a.   b.   c.   d.   e.   f.

4

a.   b.   c.   d.   e.   f.

Baby Shark and the Tooth Fairy

That night during his dreams, Baby Shark danced with the Tooth Fairy all night.

As Mummy Shark had promised, he got a new tooth, so sharp and bright.

The next morning, Baby Shark saw his new tooth, and he couldn't stop smiling. 'It wasn't just a dream,' cries Baby Shark. 'The Tooth Fairy is real!'

Baby Shark swims straight to his mum.
'Mum, look at this! I've got a new tooth!' says Baby Shark.

'What a wonderful tooth!'
says Mummy Shark.

'I won't worry so much the next time
I lose a tooth!' says Baby Shark.

'See you then, Baby Shark!'
says the Tooth Fairy.

The end.

Baby Shark snap!

Make your own Shark Family card game. Use the template below to help you. Ask a grown-up to help you draw and cut out your own cards. You need three cards of each character.

TEMPLATE

Draw a picture of the character here.

CHARACTER NAME

Make sure an adult helps you when using scissors!

SNAP!

Colour Baby Shark yellow and remember to add a star on his cheek!

BABY SHARK

SNAP!

INSTRUCTIONS

- Deal an equal number of cards to each person
- The first person lays a card face up and then the next player lays a card on top
- If a card is laid that is the same as the one on the pile you can shout SNAP!
- Whoever shouts SNAP first wins the pile
- Play continues until all the cards are gone

56

EXAMPLES AND TIPS!

Make Mummy Shark pink and give her some big eyelashes!

MUMMY SHARK

Daddy Shark is blue with big teeth!

DADDY SHARK

Grandma Shark is orange. Don't forget to draw in some glasses!

GRANDMA SHARK

Grandpa Shark is green with a big moustache!

GRANDPA SHARK

William needs to be small and orange with big eyes!

WILLIAM

Give Baby Turtle a dark green shell!

BABY TURTLE

Baby Seahorse is pink like Mummy Shark, but she looks very different!

BABY SEAHORSE

Baby Whale is easy to draw. Don't forget to give him a big happy smile!

BABY WHALE

Fish Bus needs some wheels to drive around on!

FISH BUS

Colour with numbers!

Can you colour in the sharks using the number guide to help you?

1 White		**5** Light blue		**9** Brown	
2 Yellow		**6** Pink		**10** Dark green	
3 Orange		**7** Purple		**11** Light green	
4 Dark blue		**8** Red			

Busy ocean

The ocean can be very busy!
Colour everyone in. You're going
to need lots of different colours!

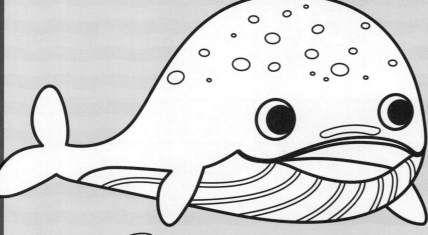

How many...

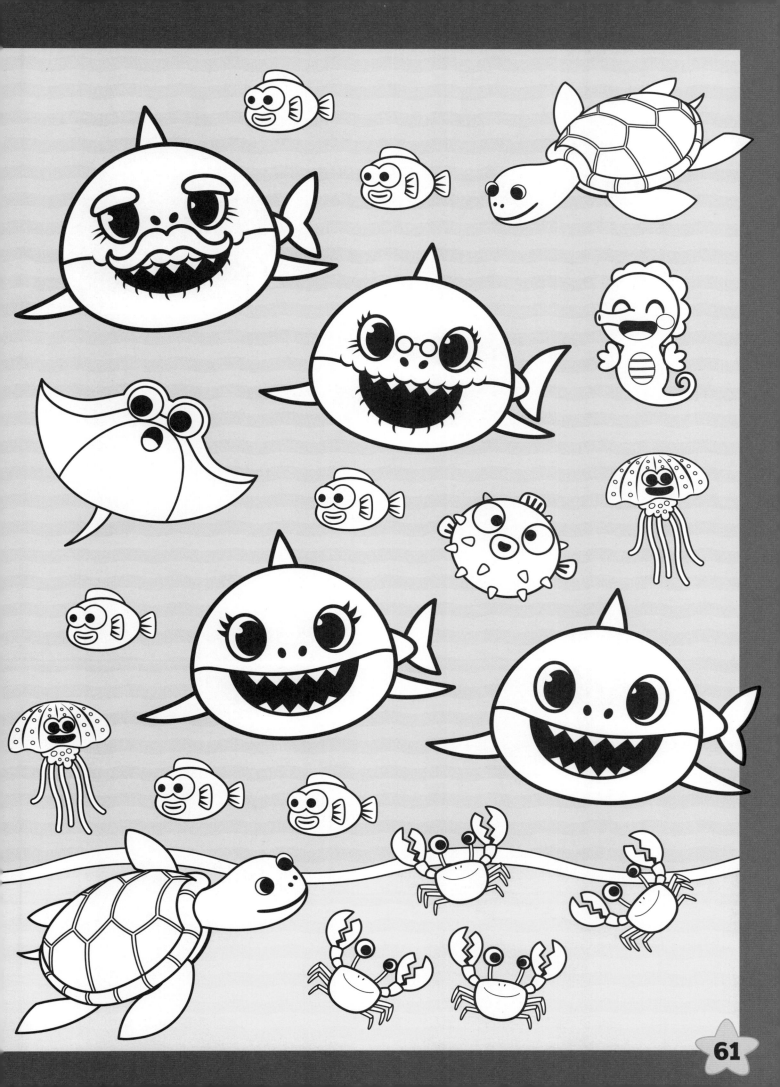

Finding the way home

Can you help Baby Shark find his way back home to his family?
Follow the arrows and guide him along.

	1	2	3	4	5	6
A	START: →					
B						
C						
D						
E						
F						

Follow the direction of the arrows to find the way. Each arrow is one box across, up or down.

7   8   9   10

Baby Shark lives at square

_____.

Who am I?

Guess who these characters are from the clues they give you.

A

I wear glasses.
I like to build sandcastles.
Mummy Shark is my daughter!

I am:
_____

B

I love to bake clam buns.

I have a moustache.

Mummy Shark is my daughter, too!

I am:
_____

C

I love to play with my son.
I'm blue in colour.
Baby Shark is my son!

I am:
_____

D

I love to paint pictures.
I'm pink in colour.
Baby Shark is my son, too!

I am:
_____

So many words!

How many words can you make with the letters from Hammerhead Shark? There are a few suggestions ready for you!

HAMMERHEAD SHARK

ham

head

Four words:
GOOD WORK

Eight words:
AMAZING

Twelve words:
SUPERSONIC!

Copycat!

Can you copy what Mummy Shark has painted for her picture? Start with the eyes first!

Where do you go?

Grandpa Shark wants to find out where Baby Shark is hiding. Which line is going to lead to him?

Shadowy sea creatures

The ocean can be a dark and strange place. Can you help Baby Shark identify the shadows of these sea creatures? Draw a line to show what each one is.

Who is next?

Can you draw the next character in the line up?

1

2

3

4

Birthday picnic

It's Mummy Shark's birthday and Daddy Shark has forgotten the cake! Can you draw a huge birthday cake in? You can decorate it how you like!

Colour in the Shark Family.

Can you remember?

Take a good look at the items on the picnic blanket. Now close the book and tell someone the items you remember or write them down. How many did you remember?

2–4 items:
GOOD WORK!

5–7 items:
BRILLIANT!

8–10 items:
AMAZING!

11–12 items:
GENIUS LEVEL!

Learn to draw!

Mummy Shark is a great artist and loves to teach Baby Shark. Can you learn how to draw Baby Shark?

1

Using a pencil draw a slightly squashed oval shape for Baby Shark's head.

2

Add a curved line to show the top and bottom half of his face.

3

Draw in 2 circles for Baby Shark's eyes and add a top fin.

4

Add pupils to his eyes – don't forget to include a cut-out shape for the highlights. Colour them in black.

5

Add nostrils and a semi-circle mouth.

6

Add 5 pointy teeth and a tongue. Don't forget to add Baby Shark's star on his cheek.

7

Add a shape as shown for Baby Shark's body.

8

Then add 2 flippers, a tail and his tummy area.

9

Rub out the join areas as shown below.

10

Now darken the outlines of Baby Shark and colour him in.

Draw your own Baby Shark and colour him in.

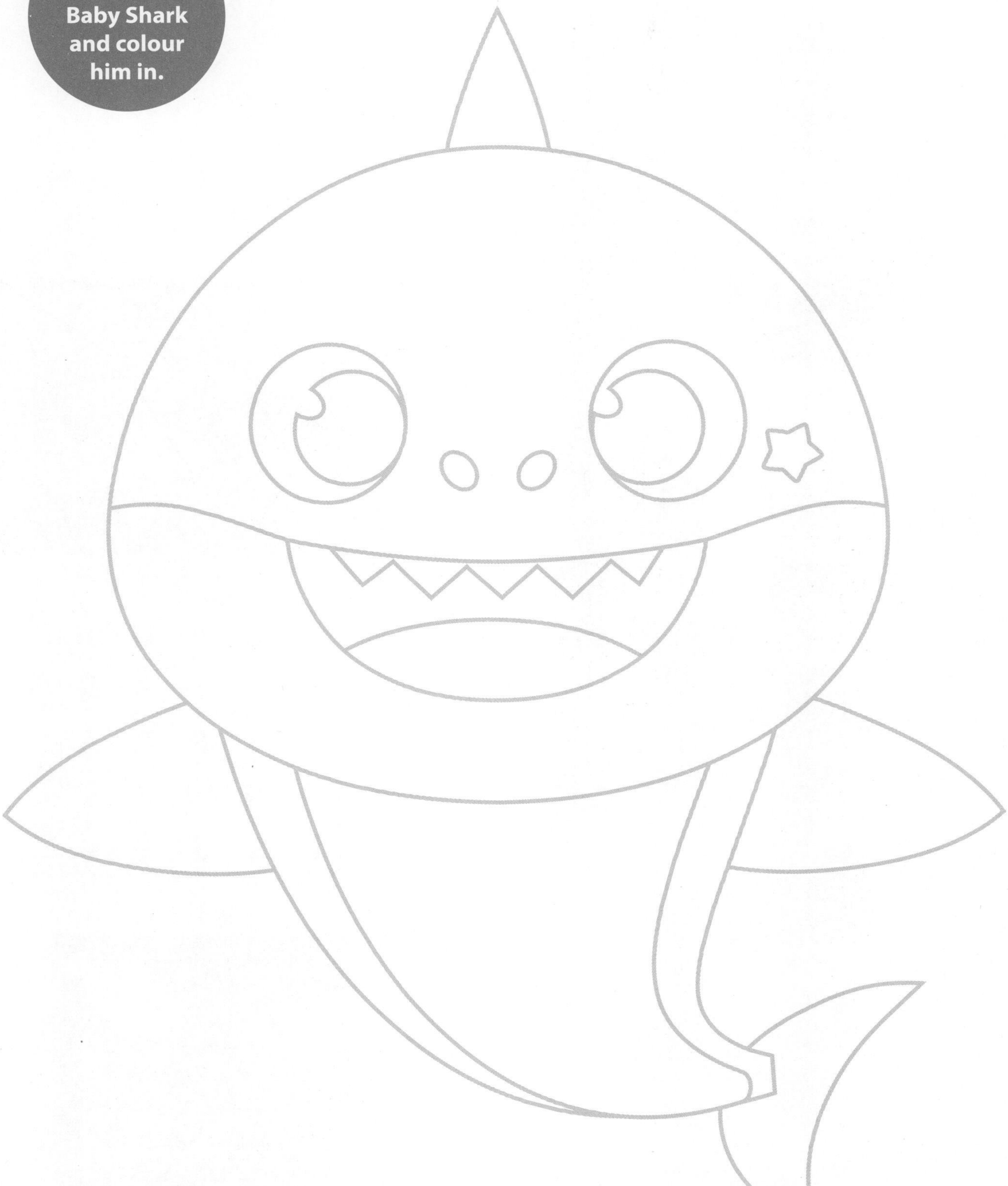

Answers

Page 14

1 = d.   **2** = a.   **3** = b.   **4** = c.

Page 15

Mummy Shark hid the cake.

Pages 24–25

Page 26

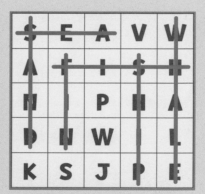

Page 27

COME FOR A PICNIC

Page 45

Page 46

Page 47

Pages 60–61

Pages 62–63

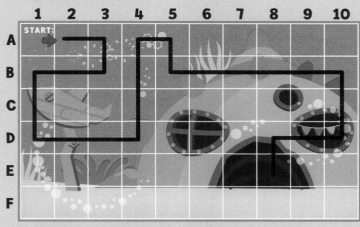

Baby Shark lives at square E8.

Page 64

A Grandma Shark
B Grandpa Shark
C Daddy Shark
D Mummy Shark

Page 65

HAMMERHEAD SHARK – here are some of the words you might have got: hammer, head, shark, he, she, me, shark, shard, mad, had, mark, hark, ram, dam, ham, am, sham, read, heed, seed.

Page 67

Line 2 leads to Baby Shark.

Page 68

1 = d.	**2** = g.	**3** = e.	**4** = b.
5 = f.	**6** = a.	**7** = c.	**8** = h.

Page 69

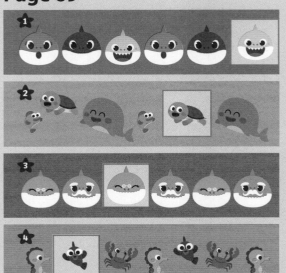